THE SUAVE, SOPHISTICATED MAN you see on the cover is not Jack Douglas' brother.

THE SUAVE, SOPHISTICATED MAN YOU SEE ON THE COVER OF THIS BOOK is Jack Douglas.

Until recently he was head comedy writer for "The Jack Paar Show," and in the past he has written material for Bob Hope, Red Skelton, George Gobel, Jack Benny and other famous comics, incidentally picking up a TV Emmy Award along the way.

MY BROTHER WAS AN ONLY CHILD w_____ _____ _____lished at $2.50
b_____ _____
9_____

Other Books by the Author

H. G. Wells' "Outline of History"

"Das Kapital"

"Das Kapital at Yale"

"Stella Dallas" (The story of a blind olive and its seeing-eye pimento)

Plays

"Mau-Mau Luau" or "Please Don't Eat Jean Kerr"

MY BROTHER WAS AN ONLY CHILD

by Jack Douglas

Introduction by Jack Paar

PERMABOOKS • NEW YORK

This Permabook includes every word contained in the original, higher-priced edition, plus new material written especially for this edition by the author. It is printed from brand-new plates made from completely reset, clear, easy-to-read type.

MY BROTHER WAS AN ONLY CHILD

E. P. Dutton edition published April, 1959

PERMABOOK edition published April, 1960
2nd printing.......................April, 1960

L

Copyright, ©, 1959, by Jack Douglas. All rights reserved. This PERMABOOK *edition is published by arrangement with E. P. Dutton & Co., Inc. Printed in the U.S.A.*

PERMABOOK editions are distributed in the U.S. by Affiliated Publishers, Inc., 630 Fifth Avenue, New York 20, N.Y.

PERMABOOK editions are published in the United States by Pocket Books, Inc., and in Canada by Pocket Books of Canada, Ltd.—the world's largest publishers of low-priced adult books.

To Gladys, beloved third harpist with the New York Philharmonic, in memory of those happy hours we spent together inside your empty harp trunk

Introduction

by JACK PAAR

(Mr. Paar is the famous ad libber.)

JACK DOUGLAS is the most imaginative writer in television. In a field where there is little honor or integrity, Jack Douglas is loaded with both. Leaving out honor and integrity, I have seen Mr. Douglas loaded but I quickly point out that this was not his fault but was caused by the evils of an expense account. I think it would be fair to say that Mr. Douglas does all his writing under the influence of money.

Women find Mr. Douglas very attractive—nearly all of his wives are my best friends. He has had more rice thrown at him than anyone I know. For many years I thought he had dandruff or perhaps at one time had been a geisha boy. He has heard more organ music at his own weddings than any daytime quiz MC. Mr. Douglas explains his compulsion for tripping the slow fantastic as better than having no fan club at all.

To describe his appearance is difficult. There are times when he is very sophisticated and looks like he

KNOWS what became of Sally. There are other times when he seems puzzled by the sane world around him and looks like a bullfighter that dropped his sword.

Even though Mr. Douglas steals paper clips from NBC he has great strength of character. I have seen him "give up smoking" time and time again. He drinks so much coffee that one time in the Luxor steam room I saw him percolate. Nevertheless, I am pleased to be best man at his new book, because I like Jack Douglas, and I am probably the only person who *really knows* what makes him "tick." It's very simple. Many years ago he swallowed a small boy who was wearing a wrist watch.

Preface

LIKE I was saying to my wife, Fromkess Schmidlapp (the noted woman authoress—*Inside John Gunther*, $3.75 at any likker store) this morning, History should be recorded by some responsible person. Things are pretty well mixed up nowadays, just as they were after the first World War, and also after the Civil War, or as some prefer, "The War Between the States" or "Someone has to pick the cotton" or, as they say in Russia, "Someone has to squeeze the sturgeon."

Of course, the Civil War was more confusing than most because Mathew Brady kept getting in the way. People got credit for things they didn't say or do at all. Barbara Frietchie didn't say that famous phrase. My old grandmother did. My dear, sweet grandmother stuck her head out of the window and yelled: "Shoot if you must this old gray head!" And by golly . . . they did! Granny usually wore bangs after that.

History has always been a puzzle to the younger generation. Now, take my offspring (a mongoose by a previous marriage). Junior froths at the mouth when he reads history, but that's a bad example—he frothed before he could read history. Let's take the Trojan War instead. What happened after that? There they were with a great empty horse outside the city, and even the non-aesthetes admitted it was facing the wrong way . . . despite the glory of a Greek sunset. It was very confusing and no matter how much the Trojans kicked it around, the big horse didn't get lost. I'm not making this up either. It's all there in mythology. My wife, Fromkess, wrote a book about it called *Pleeza Don't Squeeza da Banana*. And by the way, you must read my wife's latest book *Pleeza Don't Squeeza da Fromkess*.

—JACK DOUGLAS

THIS BOOK BANS BOSTON

CHAPTER ONE

Mother

THE WINTERS were long and very cold in the Big Smokies. They were pretty lousy in the Little Smokies, too. That's why we lived in the Catskills.

The Catskills were full of legend. In the summer when the thunder thundered the old-timers used to sidle up to me and say, "You know what that is, Sonny?" And when I'd say, "Yes, it's the little men bowling with Rip Van Winkle," they'd laugh like loons and roar, "No, you damn fool . . . that's thunder!"

The night I was born the little men were bowling with old Rip, and it was thundering, too. Mother didn't make it to the hospital. I was born on the bus. Mother was furious when she had to open her pocketbook the second time.

CHAPTER TWO

Dad

WHEN I first met John Huston I was quite impressed. He was standing in Harry's New York Bar, smoking a lizard.

My father never met John Huston. My father died when he was six years old.

A few years later I met my father for the first time. It was early one morning and I was just sitting down to a bowl of buffalo chips (they're shot from buffalo), when in walked my father. He handed me the cream and sugar and introduced himself. It seems that he had been away entertaining the troops in the War Between the States. (This was the year 1863.) I found out later that Father was quite a favorite among the boys in blue, in fact, he was known as the Bob Hope of Appomattox. Sometimes, it was rumored, he wore kilts and was also known as the Elsie Janis of Bull Run.

Besides his talent in the entertainment world, Father was the business genius of his day. He sold used scalps to the Indians. Later he traveled with a medicine show and sold "People Oil" to snakes.

CHAPTER THREE

La Goulue and Valentin*

IN ACCORDANCE with his last wishes, Daddy's ashes were scattered over Hyde Park.

Then came the reading of the will. Daddy, being of sound mind and body, left me his entire collection of vulgar gestures, plus a one-third interest in a chain of wishing wells. Mother was also mentioned in Daddy's will, but rather unflatteringly, I thought.

* A famous French dance team who, for a few francs, were very kind to me.

CHAPTER FOUR

Valentin and La Goulue*

WHEN I was a child, it was the winter that I hated most. All the other children in our neighborhood had little red sleds. Mine was *beige*. That's when I first noticed the pains.

* Famous Swiss mountain climbers, who were very kind to me, until the year 1903, when they fell exhausted in the Alpine snow and were eaten by St. Bernards.

CHAPTER FIVE

Valentin, La Goulue and Ocean~View*

AFTER DADDY DIED, Mother tried to get work as a model. She posed in the nude for a famous New York photographer but unfortunately he didn't look up from his newspaper. As a result, Mother has been barred from the lobby of the Plaza Hotel for life.

Some years later, I joined the sleeping-pill-of-the-month club. During the initiation I swallowed four bottles of nembutal laced with seconal in a full glass of warm milk. Needless to say, I missed breakfast. I also missed lunch, low tea, *high* tea, cocktails and World War II. (Incidentally I saw World War II in the movies and I was very disappointed. It was *nothing* like the book.)

I *still* had the pains, but by this time they were beginning to make sense.

---

* Names of Fire Island summer cottages.

CHAPTER SIX

1863 Was My Big Year

IF I LIVE to be thirteen, I'll never forget the year 1863. That was the year my Uncle Flaminio, while serving with the boys in blue at Shiloh, fell asleep on guard duty—Lincoln didn't pardon him, and he was placed in front of a firing squad and promptly shot. (I'm sorry, Mr. Sandburg, but you *had* to know *sometime!*)

All this, of course, happened during our Great Civil War. And it *was* a *Great* Civil War. Don't you ever forget *that!* That was one war that had *everything!* A great story, a great cast, great music, and great *movement,* thanks to George Abbott.* *My Fair Lady,* indeed!

1863 was the year that I found romance for the first time. Lovely girl, Desirée. Too bad she moved to Johnstown just three days before the flood.

* Well-known sober director.

CHAPTER SEVEN

A "Tim Snopes" Story

THE LAST TIME I saw Old Tim Snopes he was just a shell of his former self. In fact, when you held him up to your ear you could hear the ocean.

At the age of forty-six Tim Snopes, as usual years ahead of his time, was fifty-three. It really didn't matter because he was a millionaire many times over. He owned railroads, oil fields, banks, motion-picture studios, apartment houses, air lines, and he had just made a deal with the Hilton Hotel chain for two thousand miles of shower curtain. What Tim Snopes didn't own, he'd made a down payment on. (Which was pretty good for a man who had started out in life as an apprentice baby.)

From his appearance, you'd never know that Tim Snopes was one of the richest men in the world. No matter what the occasion, he always wore the same outfit—torn sneakers, ragged Bermuda shorts, and a double-breasted vest of live cats.

Tim Snopes was not only enormously wealthy, but overwhelmingly philanthropic. In 1932 he donated a new wing to the Dr. Crippen Memorial Library. In

1936 he donated another wing to the same library. In the fall of 1937, the whole thing took off and flew south.

But Tim Snopes's great empire is no more. The once mighty tycoon is now spending his remaining years in quiet seclusion at "Merde-view," his lovely old twenty-five-room tent, on a lovely grass-shaded lane, on lovely Fire Island, forgotten by all, except a few old and treasured friends like Nefertiti, Floyd Collins and the June Taylor dancers.

This is *my* favorite Tim Snopes story—I hope it's *yours*.

Sunday Morning in Arizona

SUNDAY MORNING in Arizona is just like Sunday morning in Connecticut only more bowlegged.

Poughkeepsie Under the Czar

AT THE TIME we moved to Poughkeepsie, Ivan the Terrible was the Czar. He was very cruel to the Peasants (of Poughkeepsie). Every winter he would strip ten virgins* in the public square (just opposite the Mort Rat Tearoom**). The cruel Czar would then pour ice water over the ten virgins and freeze them into living statues. The Czar enjoyed these off-Broadway Ice Capades immensely until one particularly cold winter when he tried it on Gypsy Rose Lee. As soon as the water froze, she turned to the Czar, smiled sweetly and started to strip—an ice cube at a time. Ivan the Terrible was furious. Gypsy was banished to Siberia, where she wrote a helluva book about sex and salt mining.

In Poughkeepsie, December 18, 1899, will always be known as the day of terror. I remember the date well. That was the day the Samovar Roebuck cata-

* See U.S. Government pamphlet #869425J.
** Duncan Hines died here.

22

logue arrived. It was also the day the Cossacks arrived. They smashed down our front door with their sabers. Their leader, a vicious, Mongolian-type heel named Bubnov stalked into our parlor. First he kicked me in the groin, then he asked an uncivil question. Then he kicked Grandpa in the groin, then he kicked Grandma in the groin, then Grandma kicked Grandpa in the groin. (It was a gala day for the Trenton Truss Company.) Just then my beautiful sister (Maria Tallchief) came into the room. Bubnov's cruel mouth twisted into an ugly leer. Spittle ran down his chin and overflowed his spittle catcher. With the snarl of a wild beast he lunged at my beautiful sister (Maria Tallchief) and dragged her through the door into the night. Her screams made my blood run cold. We stood there knowing it was useless to try to help her. Finally it was over. The next time I saw my sister (Maria Tallchief), she and Bubnov were married and living in Scarsdale.

CHAPTER TEN

Vodka!
or
Under the Tables Down at Mory's

BEFORE WE GET too far from the Czarist reign in Poughkeepsie, a few words about vodka. As my beautiful sister once said: "Vodka is the curse of the Russian people."

As you probably all know, vodka is made from potatoes, and drunk by the peasants to give them strength—to plant more potatoes. Vodka is the most powerful drink in all the world. When you hear someone order three fingers of vodka you realize immediately that he must have spilled some on the other two. Vodka is an excellent pain-killer, but it is also the assassin of ambition. It has been the downfall of many of my people. Of course, there are some who do not agree. As a famous Czarist madam once said: "It ain't the vodka that kills you . . . it's them goddam steppes!"

CHAPTER ELEVEN

The Year the Locusts Came

THE YEAR 1856 was a black year in the history of the Snoqualomy Valley. That was the year the locusts came. The year the locusts came will never be forgotten by the farmers who tilled the soil in the Snoqualomy Valley, and forever after, in the Snoqualomy Valley, the year 1856 was known as "The Year the Locusts Came."

"It don't seem possible," remarked P. John Martin, head of the Chamber of Commerce. "It just don't seem possible that just ninety years ago, in the year 1856, that here in the sun-kissed Snoqualomy Valley the locusts came."

"But they did," replied his wife. "The locusts did come in 1856, and nobody will ever forget that year that the locusts came."

And nobody ever *did* forget. Except, maybe, a few crummy locusts.

CHAPTER TWELVE

The Age of Unchivalry
or
Chastity~Belt Keys Made While You Wait

THE OTHER DAY in one of the more prosperous communities that line the eastern tip of Long Island, a man was arrested for Petty Puberty, a rather obscure law that forbids the transportation of trained female seals over the state line for immoral porpoises. This is just one more example of our ever-increasing lack of courtesy. As Voltaire once put it, and very well, too:

"Ich habe meinen Zug verpasst!"

Nevertheless, I think that this cunningly *calculated understatement* will bring about a more complete understanding, if not amongst nations, at least among those whose duty it has been and, let us hope, it shall always be, to uphold and defend (yes, to the end if need be) the tradition and sacred rituals of a group that, although they have long since vanished

26

from the face of the earth, will live everlastingly, in the hearts of all of us who have known what it is.

I think, I may also say, with deadly fear of contradiction, that although the seasons may seem to change from cool to warm to cool, and then to cold, this is an illusory vision, usually the permanent possession, and very well-guarded secret, of the uninformed, of which, unfortunately, there are still too few, even in this day of mass heredity.

This, of course, takes us back to our basic thought, that even though we don't agree with what Voltaire said, we must defend to the death his right to say it, because he was a very sick man at the time.

CHAPTER THIRTEEN

Philadelphia, Pennsylvania

PHILADELPHIA is two hours from New York by train, and thirty-five minutes by telephone. Philadelphia was laid out by William Penn and from all reports it still is. Philadelphia's most famous citizen was Benjamin Franklin, who discovered electricity while flying his kite during a violent lightning storm. Franklin's discovery not only changed the whole course of human events, but it also changed Ben from a baritone to a soprano. (Which of course opened up the way for him to become an exchange student with Sweden—Stockholm got Ben and we got Jenny Lind.)

Benjamin Franklin probably is most famous for his homely little philosophies such as "Early to bed, early to rise, makes a man healthy, wealthy and wise" and "A stitch in time saves nine" and "Never trust a naked bus driver."

Philadelphia was first called the "City of Brotherly Love" by a man named Dudley Hartrampf, who was later drawn, quartered, hanged, stabbed, shot and burned at the stake, between Eighteenth and Nineteenth on Chestnut Street for double parking.

The Year the Locusts Came

(See page 25.)

The Private Mitty of Walter Thurber

MOST MEN go through life sharing a mitty, but not Walter Thurber. Walter would rather be found dead before he'd share a mitty with anybody. For thirty-six years he'd worked and saved and scrimped and denied himself, and finally he had enough money to have a private mitty all his own. To Walter, it was like a seat on the stock exchange—expensive, but well worth it. Anyway, it was worth it to Walter Thurber. Everywhere he went, out of the corner of his eye he could see people nudging each other and whispering in awed tones, "There he is—the only man in South Norwalk with a private mitty."

Of course, no one would ever have heard of Walter Thurber outside of South Norwalk if he hadn't fallen in love with Ethrelda Boober, the third. Ethrelda was an exquisite thing. Lovely pale shoulders with Shalimars to match. Walter met her one night in the cocktail lounge of the Greyhound bus station, where he was killing time while waiting for a Martini.

30

Later that evening on the outskirts of South Norwalk, Walter, in a fit of suburban passion, murdered the lovely Ethrelda. No one would ever have heard of this murder, outside of South Norwalk, either, if it hadn't been for Walter's fiendish ingenuity in accomplishing the foul deed. He simply painted a telephone on her body, then dialed her with an ice pick.

The trial lasted forty-four days. Walter based his whole defense on his private mitty, but it didn't help. He was convicted and hanged.

Ever since I first told this story, people have asked me what in hell is a private mitty? Let me answer that question with this little anecdote of one of Walter's last few days on earth:

After the trial, Walter was being transferred from the county jail to the Charlestown prison, where the gallows awaited him. Passing over the Connecticut River bridge at Old Lyme, Walter suddenly reached inside his coat, pulled out a milk bottle he'd concealed there and flung it over the railing and into the river. Thirteen years afterwards this very same milk bottle was picked up by an English-speaking native on the rugged coast of Madagascar. Curiously he plucked out the crumpled note inside the bottle, his lips moved as he slowly read the faded message:

"Please leave two quarts."

Famous Bastards

(What's the use—you *all* know
who you are.)

The Story of Wine
or
Brown Feet, Why Are You Blue?

THE STORY OF WINE is a very interesting one, especially if you tell it with a magnum handy. The story of wine goes back four or five thousand years to the little town of Nutley (rhymes with Gutley), Saudi Arabia, which is a little town on the Red Sea. Or, I should say, it *was* a little town on the Red Sea. It was so small, it's not there any more. The mice ate it.

In this little town there lived a man by the name of Of. Of Jones was the father of wine. (He was also the *mother* of wine, but that's another story.) The whole thing started as many improvements do, by accident. Of was walking through a cow pasture one day and he spied a wild grappa vine, just lousy with wild grappas. Of decided right there and then to make wine, so he filled his apron with wild grappas (no mean feat since he was 102-per-cent nude).

33

That very night in the basement of his little hut, Of made wine. Running through the grappas in his bare feet he squeezed the juice into small-mouthed bottles, later to be sold to wide-mouthed people. When the wine was ready, Of opened up the first Copacabana. The wine was an instantaneous success. ~~Every Sob~~ and his sister were drunk. (They didn't have brothers in those days.) But Of Jones, the creator of this sparkling nectar of the gods, was the drunkest of them all. Poor Of couldn't move a muscle. He just lay there . . . with the eyes of Texas upon him. His friends didn't know what to do. Finally, someone, as more of a gesture than anything else, kicked a little dirt over him. Then others kicked a little dirt over him. The hobby caught on. People were now kicking dirt over poor Of in droves. Excursion trains were run in. Round-the-world luxury liners changed their course for the accommodation of passengers who wished to join in the fun. Pilgrims faced west instead of east. Overnight Mecca's Neilsen went down six points. Kicking dirt over poor Of Jones had become an international pastime, but did Of Jones take it lying down? Yes. And by spring of 1908 he was covered with four trillion, eight hundred and forty-eight million cubic tons of well-kicked dirt, called the Berkshires. Twelve years later, the skeleton of Of Jones was found by some Boy Scouts while digging for Girl Scouts. They brought it out into the sunlight, propped it up against a tree and ran off to report their find. A few minutes later the skeleton's bony hand slowly moved up and covered the staring eye sockets of the shining skull.

"Jeez," mumbled Ol Jones. "What a hangover!"

You can be as tall as she is—stand
on her kneecaps.

CHAPTER EIGHTEEN

The Boy Who
Cried Dinosaur

LITTLE JOHNNY LAUDERBINN was just like all the other little boys in his neighborhood, in the little New Jersey town of Tom's Lake. He read the Koran, walked on fire, stuck hatpins through his cheeks (all of them), and every Sunday he attended the human-sacrifice ceremony at a neighboring Stonehenge. (Little Johnny was an orthodox Druid.)

The only thing *really* different about little Johnny Lauderbinn was his imagination. He had a terrific imagination and this would sometimes get him into trouble, because he used to make up stories and tell them as the truth. So, of course, after a while nobody believed a word little Johnny said.

This was a very unfortunate and dangerous situation, as we shall soon see when we accompany little Johnny to his favorite playground, the Big Swamp.

And a big swamp it was. Big and dark and, to Johnny, extremely interesting. He spent most of his time there, talking to his little friends, the frogs. The little frogs finally got to know little Johnny quite well, because he used to shoot them through the head with his .22 rifle. The surviving little frogs thought this was a *real lousy* trick, but they never did anything about it—mainly because little Johnny was the only little boy they knew who was nice enough to talk to them.

One dismal spring day, while little Johnny was conducting his little combination open forum and frog massacre, he was aware of something breathing very heavily and very high in back of him. After he turned around, he wished he hadn't. There, in the center of the swamp, wallowed a Brontosaurus, the largest of the dinosaurs. At first, even little Johnny's *imagination* refused to believe it. But it was true, the huge snakelike head more than sixty feet in the air and the multitonned body, half covered with mud and slime, were not more than fifty yards away from little Johnny's astonished eyes. His first *untangled* thought was to maybe strike up a conversation, as he'd done with the little frogs. But *what,* thought little Johnny, the hell would you *say* to a Brontosaurus? "How's the weather up there?" "Take me to your leader?" or "Don't call us—we'll call you?" Johnny rejected all thoughts of conversation when the monster suddenly heaved itself free of the sucking swamp and crunched its way to a shuddering bit of high ground.

"Mother! Mother! Mother!" screamed Johnny as he stumbled into the kitchen, "I saw a dinosaur in the swamp! A terrible horrible dinosaur!"

"I hope you weren't playing with it, dear," his mother replied. "Doctor Mosby says they carry germs."

That's the way it was. For the first time in his life, little Johnny Lauderbinn had told the truth. He told everybody in Tom's Lake about the dinosaur, but nobody believed him. This made little Johnny seethe with anger. Okay, he thought to himself, if *that's* the way they want it!

Bright and early little Johnny was back in the Big Swamp with a bag of peanuts. He ignored the friendly greetings of his friends, the little frogs, and went directly to the spot where he had last seen the Brontosaurus. And there he was, looking, if possible, even larger and more terrifying in the bright morning sun. Johnny whistled, like you would to a dog, and instantly the monster's huge body tensed, its head, high in the air, snaking from side to side. Johnny whistled again and held out the bag of peanuts. The Brontosaurus froze.

"Peanuts," explained little Johnny.

The Brontosaurus didn't move.

"Don'tcha *like* peanuts?" asked little Johnny.

The Brontosaurus didn't answer.

"Okay," said little Johnny. "If you don't want 'em, I'll eat 'em *all* myself!"

Immediately, the Brontosaurus wanted one.

As the days passed, the Brontosaurus became very fond of little Johnny and his peanuts. This huge creature, little Johnny quickly learned, would do *anything* for a peanut. The Brontosaurus, according to the encyclopedia, has *two separate* brains, but even so, the sum total of the two, added together, gave the Brontosaurus an I.Q. of minus three. Nevertheless, little Johnny was careful to treat this simple-minded monster with utmost respect. He figured, stupid or not, anybody with fourteen-ton feet was not to be trifled with. (One wrong word to a Brontosaurus, and you'd be a long time flat!) And little Johnny wasn't taking any chances. He had big plans for this monstrous pet of his. Because little Johnny hadn't forgotten the jeering laughter that had come from all sides, when he had told about the Brontosaurus in the Big Swamp. Even from his very own family.

In late August, little Johnny felt he was ready to put his plan into action. His peanut-trained Brontosaurus responded to his every command promptly and without question.

It was a very warm full-moon evening. Little Johnny, his mother, father and his older brother and sister were rocking on the front porch. They were practicing togetherness and so far (*that* evening any-

41

way), it had been working out pretty well. An unfamiliar air of sweetness and light filled them all. They were at peace with the world. And each other. Little Johnny waited for an appropriate silence. Finally, just as the moon disappeared behind a small cloud, he said softly:

"Saw a dinosaur in the swamp today."

"What kind of a dinosaur?" asked his brother, going along. "There are several different species, you know."

"I know," replied little Johnny. "This one happens to be a Brontosaurus."

"I hope you weren't playing with it, dear," his mother interjected, as little Johnny knew she would. "Doctor Mosby says they carry germs."

The whole Lauderbinn family, with the exception of little Johnny, laughed at their witty mother.

"Doctor Mosby shouldn't go around making cracks like that about a Brontosaurus," little Johnny said. "It's liable to make the Brontosaurus sore at him, and it's not a very good thing to get a Brontosaurus sore at you."

"Are *you* gonna *tell* that Brontosaurus what Doctor Mosby *said* about it?" asked his older sister, joining the fun.

"I sure am," answered little Johnny, getting up. "See you later."

Needless to say, Doctor Mosby, his lovely Cape Cod cottage, his attached garage, his rosebushes, his weeping willow, and his velvety green lawn vanished from the face of the earth. All they ever found was the good doctor's cracked bifocals, and a few peanut shells.

But that was only the beginning. Every night thereafter, little Johnny and Lolita, as he now called his prehistoric nymphet, stomped out a few more *non*believers. Systematically, a block at a time, the town of Tom's Lake was disappearing. On one particularly lucky night, little Johnny had the Brontosaurus step on the high school, during a PTA meeting.

"Group therapy," he explained to Lolita.

In no time at all the little town was nothing but a uniform series of rain-filled craters.

Little Johnny, his mother, father, older brother and sister, on another warm, summer semi-togetherness evening, were gathered on the moon-soaked Lauderbinn front porch. Little Johnny broke the silence:

"Saw a dinosaur in the swamp today." Then he held his breath in resigned anticipation.

"I hope you weren't playing with it, dear. Doctor Mosby says they carry germs."

Little Johnny hesitated, but only for a moment, then he whistled three times. Almost immediately the earth trembled. Then it jarred mightily, as the one-hundred-and-twenty-ton Brontosaurus thundered its way across the devastated town and up onto the

Lauderbinn front lawn. Little Johnny handed it a peanut.

"Step on Mother," he said.

(Suggested further reading: *Unusual Matricides,* by L. Borden.)

CHAPTER NINETEEN

To hell with Chapter 19. Every damn book you pick up has a Chapter 19.

India

or

Put the Cobra Back in the Basket, Mother— There'll Be No Show Tonight

No DOUBT now that the Chinese junk fares are so reasonable, many of you are planning a trip to India. Mysterious India. Wondrous India. Sensuous India. Indian India. India is known as the Dark Continent, that is if you just ignore Africa.

A chapter about India would be incomplete without some mention of Mahatma Gandhi, therefore let us consider this chapter incomplete, shall we?

India is famous for its belly dancers. In fact, they are very proud of their belly dancers, and the competition is very keen. I remember during a price war among the night clubs of Calcutta, one club had a big neon sign out front: "Biggest Belly in Town—Five Cents."

There are many types of bellies, Indian belly-dance experts tell me. There's the long belly, the short belly, the round belly, the bias belly and the Rajaput or the belly with the fringe on top. The most famous of all the belly dancers in India is Sally Nagpur, but due to an unfortunate accident she is now retired.

The accident occurred in the Famous Howrah Hasheesh Garden in Bombay. Sally was doing her world-famous belly dance, which incidentally is just the opposite from the can-can dance. Anyway, Sally was doing her dance to the music of *Tales of the Vienna Woods* (the Sabu arrangement). Everything was going fine. Never had Sally rippled so magnificently . . . in and out . . . in and out . . . high tide . . . low tide . . . high tide . . . low tide. . . . . Suddenly, during the snap-the-whip passage, Sally's whole career collapsed—the orchestra changed key and poor Sally dislocated her belly. She never danced again, which brings to mind that old Indian proverb:

"A boy's best friend is his mother, but a girl's best friend is her belly, providing it's got Timken bearings."

As I traveled through India, I saw many fascinating things: the fakirs, the yogis, the burning ghats, the Lowell Thomases, and the Taj Mahal, which is a

47

tomb, and incidentally the only tomb I know of with a men's room. This alone is worth the trip to India. It has jade stalls with "Out of Order" spelled out in rubies.

Famous Bastards No. 2

(See The Year the Illegitimate
Locusts Came.)

Wednesday

DEAR DIARY: Saw *her* with *him* today.

Thursday

DEAR DIARY: Saw *him* with *her* today.

Friday

DEAR DIARY: Saw *her* and *him* with *them* today.

Saturday

DEAR DIARY: Saw *her* and *him* and *them* with *those* today.

Sunday

DEAR DIARY: Shot the Easter Bunny.

Clemmys Guttata*

WHEN I first met Beardsley Trunnion, he was a turtle. He still is. That's the way of the world.

Beardsley Trunnion had come to America shortly after the Great Potato Famine. (Incidentally, he never ate potatoes even when they were plentiful.) Beardsley had come to America because he had heard that in America you could be anything you wanted to be, and although Beardsley wasn't quite sure *what* he wanted to be, he knew he didn't want to be a *turtle*. He'd *had* that.

When Beardsley Trunnion first arrived in Hollywood, he ran smack into the housing problem. Try as he would, he just couldn't find a place to live. He walked his little legs right down to the quick, which didn't take long because although turtles are long on patience, they're short on quick. Everywhere he looked it was the same story: "No vacancy!" "No Children!" "No Pets!" And then, of course, racial prejudice: "No Turtles!"

* Don't *ever* say this to a turtle!

Finally one day, when Beardsley was about to give up, he saw a "Vacancy" sign on a motel. Beardsley, and a little starlet he'd had presence of mind to pick up at a bus stop, rushed into the manager's office. Sure enough, there *was* a vacancy but, the smirking manager told them, there was a house rule, they could only stay for fifteen minutes.

Well, Beardsley thought sadly to himself, that's show business, and left.

Many weeks later, hearing not a word in answer to his desperate telegram to Norman Vincent Peale, poor Beardsley, tired, hungry and broke, decided to stick up a liquor store. Which he did, and very successfully, too. The proprietor of the liquor store was so amused by the novelty of being robbed by a masked turtle, he not only emptied the till, but he showed Beardsley where he'd hidden the receipts from the day before. Success begat success, and later that day, while molesting another young starlet, with the consent of her mother, who thought he was a talent scout, Beardsley himself was discovered by Sam Goldwyn, Jack Warner, Darryl Zanuck, Howard Hughes and Lawrence Welk.

In his first picture, Beardsley Trunnion was compared to Brando—unfortunately. The picture was a smashing flop. Even one of the most tolerant critics, Lester Glebe, of the *Arizona Globe* (Globe, Arizona) gave it only one gloob, which is pretty bad, even in Globe.

Beardsley Trunnion, the poor unknown turtle who

had emigrated to America and had become a movie star, made the one mistake he never should have made if he wanted to continue being a movie star. He *never* should have made a picture! It's little mistakes like this that have loused up quite a *few* Hollywood careers.

His acting days behind him, Beardsley turned to another career. Martinis. Turtle Martinis. (With a dead fly instead of the olive.) Beardsley Trunnion became a drunk. And there's nothing quite so disgusting as a drunken turtle. And nothing quite so hopeless.

That's about all there is to the story, except this small notice clipped from the obituary column of last week's *Variety:*

BEARDSLEY TRUNNION, age 82.
Former turtle.

For Men Only

(Hold a lighted match behind this page.)

What Every Young Girl Should Know

(Hold a lighted match behind this page.)

Dreamers!

Lentils

EARLY THIS MORNING, somewhere in between my orange juice and my number-one concubine, I got to thinking about Toynbee Doob. You probably don't remember Toynbee Doob, but he was quite well known in our town. Toynbee endeared himself to the townspeople by erecting a statue of a pigeon, in the park. (The generals came from miles around.) Toynbee will also be remembered as the man with twelve fingers. He had an extra pinkie on each hand. When Toynbee drank tea he was the politest bastard in the county.

Toynbee Doob worked at the perfume counter in the Emporium. And the Emporium carried the best assortment of perfume in town. They had perfume that made you attractive to the opposite sex and they had perfume that made you attractive to your own sex. They had perfume that smelled like new-mown hay, perfume that smelled like an Arabian harem, and perfume that had an odor of a pine forest. For as little as $2.75 a bottle, you could smell like Rebecca of Sunnybrook Farm, Scheherazade, or Paul Bunyan. But, surrounded as he was by this sea of exotic aromas, Toynbee Doob still smelled like a wolf. And he *was* a wolf. A fact known only to himself and his barber (who, once every two weeks, rounded off his ears).

Female superstructure interested Toynbee most, and he could tell the real ones from the Firestones at fifty paces.

When the fraudulent fräuleins approached his perfume counter, Toynbee coldly ignored them, but the girls with the genuine article(s) were as welcome as spring to the hills of Old Wyoming. (As a boy, in Wyoming, Toynbee had climbed one of these hills and had been *very* disappointed when he reached the top.)

Things had been pretty routine for Toynbee until he met Londa LaSalle. Londa was gorgeous. Big green eyes, jet-black hair, long elegant legs, and the way she filled a sweater! Toynbee had never in his whole life seen such *cruelty* to *cashmere!*

They were married in the little church around the corner from the little church around the corner. (Stokes Poges papers please copy.) For the first two years they were deliriously happy. Almost every day Toynbee would bring Londa some little thing. Candy, flowers, a bit of jewelry. And Londa would reciprocate by cooking the kind of food that Toynbee liked. Toynbee had a positive lust for lentils and Londa would prepare them in every inconceivable way.

Fried lentils, stewed lentils, roasted lentils, lentils à la king, lentils à la lentils, lentils smothered in lentils, under glass, under lentils, and last but not least Lentils Jubilee. Yes, Londa and Toynbee were deliriously happy until *he* came along—Sinbad Schwartz. Yes, the sailor.

Sinbad schwartzed his way into Londa's heart, and stole her away from Toynbee. They were divorced. Londa married Sinbad and Toynbee started drinking. (Scotch and lentils.) Toynbee neglected his work and got fired. Two hours later he was a bum. (Toynbee was still a fast worker.) One day in Toynbee's befogged brain a plan formed. Toynbee pawned his mother and bought a revolver. Then, one rainy night, he lurked in the shadow of a fireplug (he was a rather small man) and waited for Londa and Sinbad to come out of a penny arcade. Suddenly he saw them. They were arm in arm, and walking toward him. Steadying the revolver against the fireplug, he squeezed the trigger twice.

Years later, Toynbee Doob was *still* a bum, but if that poodle hadn't spoiled his aim, he would have also been a murderer.

CHAPTER THIRTY-ONE

CAMP NOKOPOKOPOKONOMOPKO
BRIDGETON, MAINE

Julie 17 1958

Dere Mom and Dead
          One of the kidds feel in
the lak and drown today   Herbie
was bite be a rottle snake
today   We had aple pie today
we dint have watter sking
today be cause mister monhan
brok both of one of his leggs
       so did melvin   i hop i like
the rist wach you bring me
if you cum up to see me
soon   my coonseler is a fagg
can i be one ?   i dont thimk
it cost enything xtra

                    yore sun louis

CHAPTER THIRTY-TWO

How to Train an Aardvark

AN AARDVARK is easy to train, but first for people who are a little hazy as to what an aardvark is: The aardvark is native to Africa, eats ants, and according to most anthropologists is not a true mammal, but rather a cross between a platypus and a saroyan. However, he makes an excellent pet and is easy to train. As mentioned, the aardvark catches ants and eats them. In order to do this with maximum efficiency, wondrous nature has given the aardvark Scotch tape instead of a tongue. Aardvarks make excellent watch dogs and are, of course, easy to train for this purpose. But a word of warning at this point! You are leaving yourself wide open if you put up a sign: "Beware of the aardvark." It might be more prudent to throw the whole thing on the family and have a sign: "Beware of the Smiths" or "Beware of the Shultzes" or the Trumans, as the case may be.

Another word of warning. Never tease an aardvark. They are easily trained, but they will not tolerate any tail pulling or food snatching, but if you *must* tease an aardvark you'd do well to remember— an aardvark has teeth on both ends.

Aardvarks are also easily trained as working animals. They can be hitched up to a little dog cart and taught to deliver the milk, just as you've seen dogs do in Holland. (Aren't the tulips lovely in Holland at this time of year? I have one in a bowl in my desk right now, and it does so remind me of Holland. Holland with its windmills, its canals and its huge dikes with little fingers in them.)

Aaaaaaaah well, back to the training of the aardvark, which is easy. The aardvark loves to play games. Simple games, of course, like fetching a thrown stick or ball, getting the morning paper, and also it is easy to teach an aardvark to keep an eye on the baby at night, while you and the little woman are taken in by a movie. But here another word of warning. If you leave your baby with an aardvark you must also have a sitter because although an aardvark is just crazy about ants, he also likes babies.

In closing, if you follow the above simple rules, and exercise a little kindness and patience, you will find your aardvark very easy to train. And a well-trained aardvark will give you many hours of happiness, and his cute antics will warm the cockles of your heart.

NOTE: If your cockles get too warm, rub them with dry ice.

I Never Knew Roosevelt

Doctor Murgeon, the Virgin Surgeon

TREE SURGERY, unlike training an aardvark, or an arbutus, isn't easy. First, you must learn how to make a sick tree well, then you must go to college and learn how much to charge. After graduating from college, you must serve as an interne in some small patch of brush. After two years of sawing off twigs and emptying sap buckets, you become a full-fledged tree surgeon and are ready to hang up your shingle (in whatever wood you are specializing in).

Doctor Murgeon, the virgin tree surgeon and our hero, had yet to acquire his first patient. He sat restlessly in his tiny office smoking cubeb after cubeb, waiting for the telephone to ring. He would have given anything to have a patient in the office right then. He'd even be willing to split a fee with Doctor Davey. The office door opening startled him out of his overanxious reverie. It was his nurse, Miss Eucalyptus. There was a man outside with a young birch (that's spelled right) that needed medical attention.

"Send him in," Doctor Murgeon almost shouted.

The man, a vicious-looking brute with a bashed-in nose, entered heavily, dragging a sullen-looking young birch tree with him. "Accidental gunshot wound," said the man. Doctor Murgeon laid the young birch on the operating table, at the same time informing his formidable visitor that all gunshot wounds, accidental or otherwise, must be reported to the police, and reached for the telephone.

"Don't bother!" snarled the man, whipping out an unsawed-off shotgun.

"But why shouldn't I report this to the police?" asked Doctor Murgeon, staring at the man with his Scotch-and-watery blue eyes.

"Because," replied the man, his lower lip quivering, "I'm the Chief of Police."

"Oh," said Doctor Murgeon, and whipped out his probe.

Doctor Murgeon had many cases in his long years of tree surgery. There was hardly a tree on Elm Street that hadn't been operated on by old Doc Murgeon. On quiet summer nights you could hear one tree say to the others, "Girls, I must tell you about my cement."

Cement was Doctor Murgeon's undoing. That and his extreme nearsightedness. One blustery night in November, Old Doc was called in to do an emergency appendectomy on Mrs. Cecil Fowler's weeping willow. Old Doc performed the operation in the kitchen, and despite the fact that Mrs. Cecil Fowler was expecting twins any time, and despite her physician's advice not to drink intoxicating beverages, Mrs. Cecil Fowler was lying on the kitchen floor having passed out cold. And let me say here and now that if while Doctor Murgeon was operating on the weeping willow, Mrs. Cecil Fowler had been cold sober and conscious, if nearsighted Old Doc hadn't dropped and broken his glasses, if the lights hadn't failed when the tornado took the roof off the house, it never would have happened. Poor Mrs. Cecil Fowler —instead of the weeping willow, *she* got the cement.

The next morning, in the cold gray of dawn, the willow died and Doctor Murgeon suddenly realized what he had done. He immediately grabbed a freight train and left for parts unknown.

Some weeks later, Mrs. Cecil Fowler went to the hospital and gave birth to, not twins, but triplets. A boy and a girl and a birdbath.

On One's Hand It Is Much Better to Have Fingers Than Toes

—Neiman-Marcus

ONE DAY while climbing the rope ladder to my little room on the fourteenth floor of the Pierre Hotel (the Pierre Hotel has no thirteenth floor), I got to thinking about the Gabor sisters. Everybody talks about the Gabor sisters. What about the Gabor *brothers?* Everybody talks about Cleopatra. What about the *asp?* Everybody talks about San Francisco. What about the *earthquake?* Everybody talks about Walter Pidgeon. What about the *asp?*

And so it goes, on and on. That's the trouble. Everybody talks. Nobody listens.

Now take my cousin Titus Fenn. My cousin Titus was the smartest boy in his class at Yale. He graduated with honors and was immediately taken into the most prominent law firm in New York. Two years

75

later, he was made a partner and married the boss's daughter, an old sea captain.

Titus Fenn didn't accomplish all this by sweet talk. In fact, Titus didn't talk at all. He couldn't. Titus was deaf and dumb. His vocal chords were nonexistent, and he wore nose glasses, so his ears didn't really mean a thing. Being a lawyer you'd think that he'd be slightly handicapped, but not Titus Fenn. He'd saved many a murderer from going to the chair entirely by the sign language. Titus talked with his hands and his hands spoke volumes. Many a time after a successful trial Titus' thumb would be wringing wet from the kisses of the acquitted man, his family and his friends.

Titus Fenn was one of New York's most successful barristers, until he started talking too much. He went on and on. No matter what the subject, just mention anything and he'd start running off at the hands. Titus seemed to have lost his grip, for some reason. Titus enjoyed making a spectacle of himself. He embarrassed his poor wife time and again. No matter how much she admonished him, Titus, in mixed company, would put soot on his fingers and tell dirty stories. Talking too much got Titus into all kinds of trouble. Once a taxi driver took exception to him and Titus called the man a vile name with his index finger. The driver promptly slammed the taxicab door on it, and to this day that finger has a slight lisp. At another time the loquacious Titus exposed his fingers so much on an open-top bus that he was laid

76

up for weeks with some mysterious malady, later diagnosed as digitalis. Time went on and so did Titus. Finally his wife could stand it no longer. She flew to Reno and obtained a divorce on the grounds of cruelty, incompatibility and cold hands.

MORAL: If you're deaf and dumb, don't talk out of turn or someone will give you the finger.

2ND MORAL: Push up the wall bed, Mother, I'm staying at the "Y" tonight.

Chicago, Illinois

(See Philadelphia, Pennsylvania.)

San Francisco, California

(See Chicago, Illinois.)

Big Yen, Ohio

(See your nurse.)

Appendicitis, New Jersey

(See your doctor.)

The Feud

MY GREAT-UNCLE Cosgrove (he's the one with the nest of robins instead of hair) and my great-aunt Yordan (she's the one whose tender mouth is pressed against the earth's sweet flowing breast)—well, anyway, Old Muddy-lips and me and my great-uncle Cosgrove were all sitting around, fighting the urge to remain sober, when the one-syllable conversation staggered around to famous Kentucky feuds. Uncle Cosgrove remarked that the longest and the bloodiest Kentucky feud was between the Hatfields and the Joads. Sensing that Uncle Cosgrove was about to embark upon an ancient tale of the Kentucky hills, I bit into the little vial of poison I'd been carrying under my tongue, swallowed, and leaned back to listen.

The bloody feud between the Hatfields and the Joads had all started back in 1851. It seems that Burb Hatfield wronged Becky Joad and was immediately shot by Rufus Joad, a half-nephew of Becky Joad's, on her mother's side. That is to say one of the Tennessee Joads by the name of Abacus Joad. Burb Hatfield's killing touched off a feud that was to last for sixty-three years. First to be killed, of course, was Burb Hatfield, then Jackson Joad, then Nebb Hatfield, then Hiram Joad, then Burnoose Hatfield, then Omar Joad. Once, the killing got a little one-sided, and with people who knew feuds best it was Joads two to one. The Joads were knocking off Hatfields by the carload and pine trees were getting mighty scarce in Tatum County. In fact, pine was so scarce that summer one Hatfield was buried in twenty-eight old shoe boxes.

Clayton Joad was responsible for most of the Hatfields' sudden departure for that cabin in the sky. Clayton was the best rifle shot of them all. Not only that, he was cunning. And not only that—he was a midget and he was cross-eyed. This gave Clayton a distinct advantage. Being a midget, he could lay in ambush in a dixie cup. And being cross-eyed, he could sweep the horizon and spot a Hatfield ten miles away with his panoramic optics.

The supply of Hatfields was getting mighty low. The Hatfields were desperate. They were even thinking seriously of offering prizes to the woman who begat the most children. Maybe a layette (if you'll pardon the expression) or a sugar-cured ham or something.

The Head Hatfield called a meeting. Someone had to kill Clayton Joad, the cross-eyed midget. He called for volunteers to undertake what was almost sure to be certain death. His little daughter, Nancy-with-the-smiling-face, stepped forward. Nancy-with-the-smiling-face Hatfield. Forty-six years old, and, by an odd coincidence, Nancy-with-the-smiling-face Hatfield was also a midget and she was cross-eyed. She vowed that she would hunt down and slay Clayton Joad.

For three months the grim manhunt went on. Then suddenly one day, around a bend in the trail they came face to face! Nancy-with-the-smiling-face Hatfield, the cross-eyed midget, and Clayton Joad, the cross-eyed midget! Some few days passed while they lined up their wandering pupils. Then suddenly they saw each other for the first time. So they killed each other.

"Is that *all* there is to the story?" I asked my great-uncle Cosgrove. But my great-uncle Cosgrove didn't answer.

"Is that *all* there is to the story?" I asked my great-aunt Yordan. But my great-aunt Yordan didn't answer, either. They both just sat there on the sofa, holding hands. I walked over to them, and asked the question again, but they didn't even look at me. I reached out and touched them, and almost instantaneously, they both crumbled into dust.

Apparently that *was* all there was to the story.

CHAPTER FORTY-TWO

"What the Hell's Going On in Them Bushes?"

(The Story of a Missionary)

ON THE LITTLE South Pacific island of Pago Pago, in the beautiful Beriberi-Hilton, lived the Reverend Davidson, a missionary. Becoming a Reverend had been a very simple procedure for the Reverend Davidson. He didn't even have to turn his collar around, because, although he had been born physically perfect in every other respect, his head was facing in the wrong direction.

At the risk of being called an opportunist, young Davidson went to Mississippi and enrolled at the Big Daddy School of Divinity, where the graduating class had voted him the most likely to be found dead in a motel. Alone.

Originally, the Reverend Davidson had been sent to Pago Pago as a faith pusher. (And incidentally, to get rid of a truckload of hot Bibles.)

In the twenty-three years he had worked with the

85

natives of this lovely South Sea isle, he had accomplished wonders. Especially among the women. After twenty-three long and patient years, the Reverend Davidson had finally stamped out clothing.

The Reverend Davidson's tranquil life on Pago Pago was interrupted only by the petty squabbles of the natives, and once by a shipwrecked sailor. The Reverend Davidson solved the problem of this unwelcome tourist's visit with neatness and dispatch. He simply threw a stick into a shark-filled lagoon, then taught the sailor how to play "Fetch."

After this epicurean (for the sharks) incident, the good (and tricky) reverend settled down to live out the rest of his days in quiet meditation. But *never* in the most hopeful of his quiet meditations did he ever figure on something like Sadie Thompson!

Sadie Thompson was a Jezebel, a fallen woman, and a drifter. A bit of fluffy flotsam built like a brick jetsam. Sadie as a woman had been *all things* to *all men,* and *all men* had been *nothing at all* to Sadie, because she was, above all things, a woman. (Whatever the hell that means.) She had drifted to Pago Pago on the *Kon-Tiki.* (She was the only female on the raft.*)

Sadie took a room at the hotel right next to the Reverend Davidson's, and all night long she played her Victrola. Loud and jazzy and enticing! All night

* Thor Heyerdahl: *"Now* he tells us!!!!!"

long the reverend pounded on the wall—at *first* to make her stop playing the Victrola.

Then suddenly the good reverend could stand it no longer. *This girl must be saved!* Grabbing the good book and a bowl of ice, he went to her room.

Late that night it started to rain. And it rained for days. It rained for weeks. It rained for months. It rained for years! And there they were, the good Reverend Davidson and the beautiful Sadie Thompson, cooped up together in one tiny room. But with temptation crawling all over him twenty-four hours a day, the Reverend Davidson remained firm. No matter how much Sadie pleaded with him not to send her back to San Francisco and prison, he *did* send her back. **On** her seventy-third birthday.

CHAPTER FORTY-THREE

Earn Extra Money in Your Spare Time—Raise Checks

ONE NIGHT, while crop-dusting a field of newly budded debutantes at "21," I ran into an old friend, Tully Doykes (not *the* Tully Doykes). After a few B and B's (Bourbon and belladonna), the conversation drifted around to our little old home town and our boyhood hero, Ptarmigan Psmith. Ptarmigan Psmith was born on a farm, halfway between Spottsylvania and Energine, Kansas. Ptarmigan didn't stay on the farm long. He didn't like farming, so he went into town and became head cashier of the Energine, Kansas, First National Bank. But, Ptarmigan Psmith didn't like banking either, so he took some of the bank's money and started to beat the horses and the stock market. When he first started this the sign on the bank's plate-glass window read: "Assets $47,000,-000,000,000," but Ptarmigan's judgment was very bad in his selection of horses and investments, so night after night he had to sneak to the front of the bank and erase another zero. Still no one in Energine suspected Ptarmigan until one Saturday morning when the bank had been open no more than fifteen minutes he started paying off in used peach fuzz.

Ptarmigan grew desperate. He tried to recoup by plunging deeper, but to no avail. The day the bank examiners arrived, Ptarmigan was still there, though the bank had disappeared. (Later reported to have been seen in Mexico City, stewed to the gills, with a blond I.B.M. machine on each arm.)

The bank examiners soon discovered the shortage and Ptarmigan Psmith was given a chance to do the honorable thing. They handed him a loaded Luger and hinted that he'd know what to do. He did. He shot the bank examiners.

Moral: It's easy to clean a bank in Energine, Kansas.

CHAPTER FORTY-FOUR

"Six G Strings in Search of an Old Violin Named Charlie"

A new play by Tennessee Gleckle *

The story of this play takes place entirely in the womb of an unborn lamb.
The action takes place entirely in the minds of the audience.
The lighting: low key.
The music: by Moondog.
The dialogue:

MILDRED.

But, Roger, why can't you face things as they *are*. It's been over three years now that you were killed in that plane crash.

ROGER.

I've never had any *clean* thoughts.

* A desperate friend of the author's.

MILDRED.

Have you ever stood on the edge of the Grand Canyon at dawn—it makes you realize how *big* you are.

ROGER.

I mean *really* clean thoughts.

MILDRED.

I've never seen a Sioux Indian I didn't like.

ROGER.

It's a very *round* thing.

MILDRED.

I won't wait any longer. I'll tell Fred tonight.

ROGER.

So is a ball.

MILDRED.

I saw the doctor today.

ROGER.

A very round thing.

MILDRED.

He told me I could *never* have children.

ROGER.

You're crying, Mildred. Why?

MILDRED.

The children were *with* me.

ROGER.

Good man, Doctor Frink.

MILDRED.

The best.

CURTAIN

A Good Word to Know

Conversation (kŏn′vẽr•sā′shun), *n.*
Sexual intercourse. *

Joe's Bar and Grill and Bar

JOE'S BAR and Grill and Bar is the home of the Eighth Avenue Ballet Company. The ballet is performed on a little stage in back of the bar, by a necessarily small but very talented group of Sadler's Wells rejects. Last night saw the world *première* of a new ballet, based on an old dirty joke, which they made into a Mother Goose story.

At the opening of this new ballet, tradition is thrown to the winds, and Miss Miraslava Firpo, a lovely toe dancer, comes out and whirls across the stage on her knees. (Tradition has to be thrown to the winds at Joe's Bar and Grill and Bar, on account of the low ceiling.) Exiting on a tremendous ovation and many *bravos,* Miss Firpo was followed by some guy in his bare feet. (He wasn't in the show—it was just a hot night.)

The second act of this daring new ballet was even more thrilling than the first act. Fokine Froonby, a newcomer, sprang from the wings and went into the wildest dance I've ever seen on the back of *any* bar *anywhere*. Such leaps! Such tremendous elevation! We all thought he was the greatest ballet dancer since Nijinsky, until we found out later that he'd just gotten his big toe stuck in a shot glass.

The third act of the ballet, called "Afternoon of the Thing," is set in a sylvan glade. A lovely little wood nymph, clad only in three small plots of damp moss, is being pursued through the sylvan glade, by a half-man half-goat. The reason the wood nymph is running away from the half-man half-goat, the bartender, who seemed to know this wood nymph pretty well, told me, is that although she's crazy about animals and also crazy about men, she hadn't figured on a *package* deal.

In the third act of the ballet, the crummy old witch, who hates the wood nymph, who is really a princess, gives her a vitamin shot with a dirty needle and the princess falls asleep and sleeps for a hundred years, which gives everybody at the bar a chance to order a drink.

Then the prince, who has been lurking in the washroom, dances up to the sleeping princess and gives her a kiss, which is supposed to wake her up, but it *doesn't,* because the needle was a lot dirtier than the script called for. This, however, doesn't stop the prince from dancing. He dances and dances and dances. Jumping, twisting, twirling—and finally, but unfortunately, he leaps high in the air, slaps his knees together and somehow, in the middle of a brilliant whirl, he gets his legs wrapped around each other, loses his head, comes down too fast and screws himself right into the stage. He broke both legs, but he did it beautifully.

I see at least one ballet a year. I *have* to. I promised my mother on her deathbed.

CHAPTER FORTY-SEVEN

Songs I Learned at My Mother's Knee and Other Locations

THE DAY YOU TOOK YOUR TOOTHBRUSH YOU BROKE MY HEART

THE DAY you took your toothbrush, you broke my heart, Gladys Zeckendorfer.

I didn't mind when you took the bath towels marked "His" and "Hers" and the cake of soap marked "Lever Brothers."

I didn't mind when you took your ten little fingers and your thirty-five little toes,

And your dimpled chin and your turned-down nose,

And the surrey with the fringe on top and the Jonny Mop,

And the silver and the rugs and the TV set, and the trees, and the bushes and the lawn and the driveway.

I didn't mind when you took the A train, and the hi-
fi and the low-fi and the wallpaper and the fire-
place and the fire,
And the bathtub and the baby and the St. Louis blues
and my bronzed Army shoes—
But the day you took your toothbrush, you broke my
heart, Gladys Zeckendorfer, and I miss your tufts.

CHAPTER FORTY-EIGHT

"It Is Better to Be a Poor Cat Than a Rich Dog"

(Old Birdlandian proverb)

MRS. LOVELACE was different from the other old ladies at the Happy Hour rest home. Quite different. Because she was a cat. Mrs. Lovelace wasn't a Persian cat, or a Siamese cat, or even a Burmese cat. She was just a plain alley cat. But with a heart of gold and a great love of children. Poor Mrs. Lovelace had never had any children of her own. Just kittens. That's why, one cold winter's night when she found a little baby abandoned on her doorstep, she brought it into the house, and gave it some warm milk, knowing all the time that if you let a little baby into your house and give it warm milk, you're *stuck* with it. But kindly old Mrs. Lovelace didn't mind in the least. It gave her something to *live* for. And one little baby was a lot less trouble than eight or ten kittens.

After a few years, thanks to Mrs. Lovelace's devotion and loving care, the baby grew into a fine, strong young man and enrolled at Harvard. But he wasn't very happy there because he lived in constant fear that some day his classmates would find out that his mother was a cat—and had to catch mice, in order to earn enough money to send him to Harvard.

Then one day, in his junior year, he fell in love with a beautiful Vassar girl. Being an honorable young man, he naturally wanted her to know everything about him, so one night, hoping she'd understand, he told her that his mother was a cat. The girl, horrified, became hysterical, because although she was majoring in poise at Vassar, this particular situation had never come up. And the very next day, for spite, she married a Princeton man. This was too much for the boy. He left Cambridge, drove all night to New York, and after paying the toll (he was *still* honorable), jumped off the George Washington Bridge. And that *same* night, and almost at the same hour, the girl, who had married the Princeton man for spite, found out that he was really a *Yale* man, and committed suicide (by swallowing a dry sponge and then drinking four glasses of water).

Mrs. Lovelace, the kindly old cat, was too ill at the time to be told of her son's death. And to this day she still believes that her son is an active member of the Hasty Pudding Club. Once a week, the dean mails her a box of Jello, so her illusion will never be shattered.

Yes, Constant Reader, there *is* a moral to this poignant story: "Never run over a cat—it might be some Harvard boy's mother."

Personal

YOUNG LADY with short right leg would like to meet young man with short left leg. Object: Out-of-this-world mambo.

This Side of the Disenchanted Infidel Revisited

or

There's Nothing Quite So Popular As a Dead Writer

I WAS A TENDER, naïve, inexperienced young English girl when I first met the famous writer S. Cott Gerfitzald. It happened one cold December night at the Lakeside Country Club. I'll *never* forget the moment that I first saw him. The world stood still. He was beautiful, magical, gently melancholic, and lying in the driveway. In a pool of rented blood.

"Do you know *who I am?*" he screamed at me. Being tender, naïve, inexperienced, young, and English, I didn't know whether he was drunk, or merely seeking information. After gently tucking some loose gravel around his chilled shoulders, I left him. I knew there would be *other* nights. *Other* driveways.

Early the next morning, I received forty-five dozen long-stemmed American Beauty roses, with a note saying: "Leave town, Lily Krine, or your body will be found in the Hollywood hills *and* the San Fernando valley. Signed: S. Cott Gerfitzald." No decent girl could resist this kind of an approach, so that afternoon we drove down to Malibu, and moved into a little beach cottage, so Cott could work without interruption. He had been assigned by the studio to do the screenplay of a new movie titled "The Cowboy and the Hooker" (a *more*-than-adult western), but poor Cott thought it was beneath his talents, and he was having great difficulty in getting his thoughts down on paper. But he *tried*. He would sit at his little table for hour after hour—just pecking away. But it was no use, and one day when I suggested that maybe things would go better if he had a typewriter, he slapped me across the mouth.

I shrugged the whole thing off, because Cott was a writer, and writers are different from people. *Very* different. One day on the beach, we were having a picnic, when suddenly *before* I dropped my hamburger in the sand, Cott had picked it up. It was *uncanny* how he could foretell the future. Ironically, even Cott didn't know during those calm, wonderful days at Malibu that he had only thirty-seven years left to live.

But I was happy for the first time in my life, and Cott was so kind and patient. After we had been together for quite a long time, he sent for enormous stacks of books he thought I'd like, and every night after dinner, we'd lie on the floor in front of a roaring fire, and Cott would mark passages for me to read the next day. He was very pleased with my progress, because it seemed that in no time at all, I could join in whenever *Black Beauty* or *Rebecca of Sunnybrook Farm* or *Tom Swift and His Shoe Fetish* were discussed at some of the literary gatherings we went to.

Then, of course, the inevitable happened: Cott started drinking again. It seems he'd been having trouble at the studio, and he'd been taken off a story that he hadn't even been on. I didn't realize how *much* he'd been drinking until one night he told me he was going to *walk* to Catalina, an island about twenty-five miles off the California coast. Using what little psychology I knew, I told him to go right ahead. Poor Cott. He was halfway there when he sobered up and had to *swim* the rest of the way.

S. Cott Gerfitzald isn't with us any more. He's gone to that big AA in the sky. I don't regret those years I spent with him. I don't regret one minute. Before I met Cott, I was a tender, naïve, inexperienced, young English girl. And I don't care what anybody thinks. I'm still English.

Lord Chesterfield's Last Letter to His Son

Dear Junior:
> Get lost.
>> DAD

Sleepy Hollow
or
The Headless Horseman
or
"They Went That Way, Stupid!"

IN THE little town of Sleepy Hollow there's a cemetery. And every night at midnight through this cemetery rides a horseman without any head. That's all there is to the story, but it brings these interesting questions: "How does he do it and who is he?" "Is he a friend of penicillin or an enemy of Adam hats?"

CHAPTER FIFTY-THREE

Old John

OLD JOHN was one of the most unforgettable characters I've ever forgotten. Old John wasn't always known as Old John. When Old John was young he was known as *Young* Old John. Young Old John used to be the leader of the Silver Cornet Band in our town. Of course, then he was known as "Hot Lips" Hannegan. And he really did have hot lips. One night, when he was jazzing up "You Are My Sunlamp, My Only Sunlamp," his lips got so hot his nostrils fused.

But Old John was the most unforgettable unforgettable. In the first place, Old John was a midget, which in itself was unusual because he came from a family of perfectly normal midgets. Besides his musical talent, Old John had other talents. Among these was his uncanny prowess in the field of invention. Old John invented two machines, without which there would be no civilization . . . no summit meetings . . . no Perry Como.

First, Old John invented the machine that separated the wheat from the chaff. Then, years later, after many back-breaking hours of research, Old John straightened up one day and cried: "Eureka!" At last he had contrived a machine that separated the chicken from the gumbo!

The public didn't take very kindly to this invention at first. It scared their horses. Poor Old John traveled thousands and thousands of miles trying to win them over. Day after day he demonstrated his machine in every city, village and hamlet up and down the length and breadth of the land. Day after day . . . separating the chicken from the gumbo. The chicken he would give away to the people who were hungry, but after six or seven years the gumbo became a problem. It began to pile up in unbelievable quantities. Everywhere he'd look, mounds and mounds and mounds of gumbo. Poor Old John didn't know what to do with it, until the spring of '59 when skinny girls started to wear sweaters.

Old John invented many other things. Some of them are still in use today. Old John's greatest triumph was, of course, that mechanical marvel, the steam shovel with the reinforced crotch.*

---

* EDITOR'S NOTE: This invention, needless to say, was immediately bought up by The Standard Oil Company and hidden away.

CHAPTER FIFTY-FOUR

Moonlight, Magnolias and Juvenile Delinquency

YES, WE HAD Juvenile Delinquency back in the mauve decade. It all started during the War Between the States. Every able-bodied patriotic woman was busily at work in some factory, manufacturing Lincoln stories. These women, naturally, were not in a position to keep an eye on their young daughters. Which suited the young daughters very well.

Honeychile Wildroot was one of these young daughters. Her mother worked at a war plant and her father was a preacher. Honeychile was a gay young moth, but she had flown too close to the flame. Honeychile showed up one fine day with a rumble-seat surprise, or as we say today, she was going to have a b-a-y-b-e-e.

Preacher Wildroot was aghast. What would his congregation think? What would the townspeople think? Poor Preacher Wildroot could see his whole career going right down the septic tank. He called the sheriff and the sheriff promised he would close all rumble seats immediately. Which he did, thus smothering several carefree couples.

After ordering a smock from Sears, Preacher Wildroot started to question his daughter. Hour after hour he grilled her. Finally, Honeychile, weary and sick, tearfully confessed. She blamed the whole thing on progress.

That night the hooded riders rode. They rode straight to the science lab at the university, and that night was the first time in the history of the South that a test tube was tarred and feathered.

Luncheon Treat
of the Week

THE THREE STOOGES
HAMBURGER

Just grind up The Three Stooges.*

P.S. For dessert, maybe Nelson Eddy?

* If you are a vegetarian, leave out Moe.

The Aspirin-Bottle Blues
or
Someone's Gotta Pick the Cotton

In 1902 we moved from Brooklyn to way down below the Mason-Dixon line to the little town of Crinoline, Georgia. Crinoline, Georgia, is in the Deep South —in fact, it's so deep it's up to here already. It wasn't much of a little ol' town, as little ol' towns go, but this little ol' Southern-fried metropolis was where I first met my first little ol' Southern-fried wife, little ol' Lucy-Ann-Mary-Jo-Suzy-Mae-Montgomery-Ward-Lee. It was love at first sight on my part, but alas, she was mad about another gentleman, Rhett Jukes, the black sheep of the Jukes family. (Rhett had gone to college and become a moron.) Little ol' Lucy-Ann-Mary-Jo-Suzy-Mae-Abercrombie-and-Fitch-Lee was so deeply in love with him my case looked hopeless.

Rhett Jukes and I used to go calling on Lucy-Ann-

Mary-Jo-Suzy-Mae-Hammacher-Schlemmer-Lee every Saturday night, but it wasn't much fun—three in a tub. One Saturday night, I got fed up and told Lucy-Ann-Mary-Jo-Suzy-Mae-Use-No-Hooks-Lee that she'd have to choose between Rhett Jukes and me. She chose Rhett. She said she couldn't live without Rhett, but just as I was about to join a showboat to forget, my luck changed. One night, Rhett attended one of those rattlesnake revival meetings, and suddenly, while he was running around yelling at the top of his lungs, "This little ol' rattlesnake ain't gonna bite me, cause I got religion, hallelujah!," the little ol' Episcopalian rattlesnake bit him. And right there Rhett died with his bare feet on.

The day after the funeral we were married, and that little ol' Southern gal tried to be a good wife to me, but I knew she'd never be able to erase from her memory the sad picture of Rhett Jukes lying there in his box, so there was only one thing left for me to do. One warm June night, I packed my carpet bag and silently stole out of town, never to see Lucy-Ann-Mary-Jo-Suzy-Mae-Götterdämmerung-Lee again.

How to Make a Zombie

Get her drunk.

Society Page

VERY OFTEN you've probably picked up the Sunday paper (if you have the strength), turned to the society page, looked at the pictures there and said:

"What the hell?"

And you're so right. Are society people really people? The answer is yes and no and maybe. Any more questions? So much for flippancy. Much may be said about society, especially café society, and it is usually without malice aforethought or thought aforethought. Have you often wondered why people in café society always looked bored? Why shouldn't they look bored? What have they got to look forward to? Nothing! Their philosophy is: "Eat, drink and be merry for tomorrow we eat, drink and be merry."

I've come to the conclusion that café-society people must work for hours in front of their mirrors to acquire that expression that sets in at sunset. They all look like they wished to spit but unfortunately had run out of saliva. The gentlemen usually look like they're smelling something and the ladies look like they've found it. But don't misunderstand. I like café society. That's where I met Olivia. Although Olivia wasn't strictly café society, she was beautiful. When she walked into the Persian Room that night, in a bare-midriff gown, my heart leapt. And I knew right away that she had not only beauty but brains, for she carried a book in her hand and had a reading light in her navel. She looked straight at me and seemed to undress me with her eyes, but as luck would have it I was wearing my Brooks Brothers shorts. I rushed to her side, knocking down Rubirosa on the way. It was mutual love at first sight.

We were seen everywhere together. The Stork, "21," the Copacabana, the Colony, the Latin Quarter, the Staten Island Ferry (first class). We even took the *wagon-lit* to Tenafly and back. It was heavenly. She was walking in the clouds, so I had to wear seven pairs of Adler's shoes at a time so I could be as tall as she was. We adored each other. I called her my little Poopsie and she called me Hildegarde. We discovered so many things we both liked. She just adored egg foo yung, and so did I—at first. But day after day, day after day, three meals a day, breakfast, luncheon, dinner, and a midnight snack, all she ever ate was egg foo yung. She had become a fanatic about egg foo yung. One night in some restaurant they had run out of egg foo yung. When she heard this, she started foaming at the mouth. Even when she wasn't eating it, everything reminded her of egg foo yung. Once, she cut her finger and she bled —egg foo yung. Finally, I couldn't stand it any longer. I gave her an ultimatum. I told her if I ever saw another order of egg foo yung, I would join the Foreign Legion! She had to choose between egg foo yung and me!

Well, it worked out fine. I spent six years in Morocco and she married Charlie Chan.

CHAPTER FIFTY-NINE

My Brother, Who Could Talk to Leprechauns

MY BROTHER was extraordinary even as a baby. He had whisky on his breath the day he was born. He was positively disgusted with mother and just used her as a chaser. By the time my brother was fourteen years old, he was a drunkard, pure and simple. (One of those words is superfluous.) My brother was a problem drinker. If a problem contained alcohol he'd drink it. He would drink anything liquid. One night we came home and there wasn't a drop of anything left in the house. Everything was gone—the cooking sherry, vanilla extract, a can of old varnish. Even in the Smirnoff Vodka ad the bottle was half-empty. He was a bad influence on the people he came in contact with. We sent him to a hospital to be cured and the night after the day he arrived there the place was raided. Seventy-eight people were arrested for drunk driving in wheel chairs.

My brother said he didn't like the effect of likker. He just liked the taste. But the effect it had on my brother was an awesome thing. He would do terrible and beautiful and strange things while in the arms of the Wilkins family. Once he tied two old maids together with Johnny Weissmuller (using a half hitch and a bowline). But finally his Canadian Club cotillions led to his downfall. The last time I saw my brother, he was lying in the gutter with a couple of his friends, laying the groundwork prior to opening an advertising agency.

The Leprechauns, Who Could Talk to My Brother

(See The Year the Pink Locusts Came.)

There'll Always Be a Steinbeck

THIS IS a story of the Monterey Peninsula, and one of the Monterey Peninsula's most interesting characters.

I'm not speaking of Johnny Bear or Rudolf the Rumpot, but of George the Toilet Seat. George the Toilet Seat bore this name not because of some crude whimsy of one of the Monterey Peninsula's jokesmiths, but because George the Toilet Seat was a Ubangi. And as old Judge Hooker roared: "By Crane! He looks like one!"

George the Toilet Seat didn't mind being a Ubangi. There was no discrimination against Ubangis. And for that matter, nobody had anything against toilet seats, either—or did they? George was a popular man around the peninsula. He was hard-working and industrious. He didn't keep his nose to the grindstone, but he got as close as he safely dared. George's mother and father were also Ubangis and when the three of them all started talking at once they started windmills for miles around.

George went to church every Sunday, where he came in handy during the collection. That is, he used to take up the collection until one Sunday some prankster dropped a heated penny into George's lip. Steam spouted from George's mouth and ears. The deacon started for him, but it was too late—George had already swallowed. The deacon cast his eyes heavenward and told the Lord the collection would be a little late that week.

For thirty years, George the Toilet Seat lived and worked around the Monterey Peninsula, and for thirty years carried a secret. A secret that gave the Monterey Peninsula one of the biggest shocks it ever had. One Friday night at the semimonthly dance of the Lions Club, George showed up wearing a skirt, a sweater, high-heeled shoes and four pounds of lipstick. George the Toilet Seat was a woman!

The citizens of the Monterey Peninsula were astounded. But they recovered admirably, even gallantly. Almost as one the people rose up and demanded that in deference to George's new status in the community she be no longer called what she had been called lo, these many years. They passed a resolution then and there and immediately sent it to the state capital at Sacramento. The governor called a special meeting of the legislature, and they passed an amendment that was read into the California state constitution. California's twenty-nine counties ratified it, and in less than eight months, this "new" woman had a new name—George the Female Toilet Seat.

CHAPTER SIXTY-TWO

When It's Apple-Blossom Time at Sing Sing

or

The Night Big Joe Got a Little Juice

IT WAS the night set for Big Joe Moran's execution. Big Joe sat in his cell in death row thinking. He thought of his mother, his father and he thought of his little brothers and sisters. He thought of the old gang at the pool room. Of Hank and Pete and George and Jimmy and Rodney and Bernie and Herman and Gene and Oleg and Rudolf and Randolph and Bill and Dick and Robert and Sascha and Frank and Dominick and Red and Smitty, and then he thought of—old Ned. Too bad he had had to kill —old Ned, too, when he'd held up the pool room and killed Hank and Pete and George and Jimmy and Rodney and Bernie and Herman and Gene and Oleg and Rudolf and Randolph and Bill and Dick and Robert and Sascha and Frank and Dominick and Red and Smitty, and of course—old Ned. Big Joe was sorry he had done it. There was only forty cents in the till. Big Joe mused. The irony of it. Being sent to the chair for a paltry forty cents, and the murder of Hank and Pete and George and Jimmy and Rodney and Bernie and Herman and Gene and Oleg and Rudolf and Randolph and Bill and Dick and Robert and Sascha and Frank and Dominick and Red and Smitty, and inevitably—Old Ned. And here it was, the night set for his execution, but Big Joe Moran wasn't worried. The governor would send a last-minute reprieve. Big Joe was sure of that.

Big Joe had had his last meal. Anything he desired, the warden had said. Big Joe had hominy grits smothered in hominy grits, with sowbelly aspic, topped off with a cup of Sanka (coffee kept Big Joe awake). The time was growing near. Father Crosby had come and gone. At exactly five minutes before midnight, a key was put into the door of Big Joe's cell.

"Time, Big Joe," said the warden.

"I know," said Big Joe. "And thanks for everything—it's been grand."

"Oh, that's all right, Joe," replied the warden.

Joe fumbled in his overnight bag. "Here, warden, I want you to have them. It's for being so kind . . .

it's . . . it's . . ." Big Joe's eyes were filled with tears.

"It's my two little friends. My little pet female black widow, and my little pet male scorpion."

"Oh, I couldn't," said the warden, his eyes a bit misty, too.

"Go ahead take them, warden. It's okay, they're married."

"Well, thanks, Big Joe," replied the warden, taking the pathetic gift of the condemned man.

The tragic little procession started slowly down the long corridor toward the little green door at the end.

"Steady, Joe," said the warden.

"Steady, warden," said Joe.

The little green door grew nearer as some prisoner started singing "Nobody Knows the Trouble I've Seen."

Once he was strapped into the electric chair, Big Joe was calm. He knew that reprieve from the governor would soon be there. Even after the first twenty-three-thousand-volt jolt hit him, Big Joe didn't lose his confidence. The governor had promised to look over the new evidence; he was bound to reprieve Big Joe after that. After the third jolt, Big Joe began to wonder, "What is this?" The reprieve should have been there by then. The governor just couldn't let him down. After the fourth paralysing jolt, Big Joe passed out cold and remained unconscious during the fifth, sixth and seventh subsequent jolts. Just before the eighth and final jolt, Big Joe suddenly regained consciousness. He looked around, his lower lip trembling like Jackie Cooper's.

"You know what I think, warden?"

"What, Joe?"

"I think the governor is a no-good-son-of-a bitch."

THIS BOOK IS BOUND IN
OLD MOROCCAN LEATHER—
SO IF YOUR OLD MOROCCAN
GRANDFATHER IS MISSING . . .